CAMPING

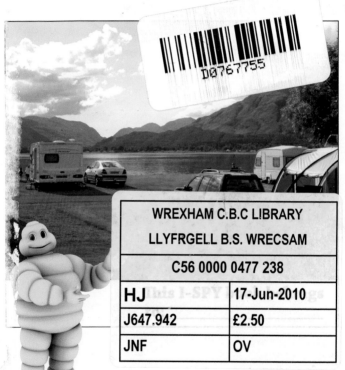

Introduction

Camping and caravanning offers a wonderful way to get away from it all, to enjoy the countryside and relax in the great outdoors. Camping continues to be hugely popular, from individual pop-up tents to large family based models that can sleep up to ten people. Don't forget the gadgets and accessories – with an electric hitch-up you can take almost everything with you, from lighting to a portable fridge. And equipment such as wardrobes, chairs and even a blow up sofa make your camping experience as comfortable as possible.

Camping doesn't have to be expensive, a good tent will last for years and you can travel wherever you want to – in this country or abroad. It's not just about sleeping close to the ground, and many people take their home with them on wheels – either with a caravan or a modern motorhome.

These methods of camping really do mean you need not leave any of your modern luxuries behind and many people travel for weeks or even months on extended holidays in them. Camping is a real family activity and there is always so much to do. Perhaps you are at a site next to the seaside, at a festival or country show. Take I-Spy Camping with you wherever you go – there will always be something new to see and spy.

How to use your I-SPY book

As you work through this book, you will notice that the subjects are arranged in groups which are related to the kinds of places where you are likely to find things. You need 1000 points to send off for your I-Spy certificate (see page 64) but that is not too difficult because there are masses of points in every book. As you make each I-Spy, write your score in the box and, where there is a question, double your score if you can answer it. Check your answer against the correct one on page 63.

I-SPY TITLES AVAILABLE:

- Ancient Britain
- At the Airport
- At the Seaside
- Birds
- Camping
- Car Badges
- Cars
- Classic Cars
- Creepy Crawlies
- Flags
- Green Britain
- History
- In the Garden
- In the Street
- London
- Modern Britain
- Nature
- On a Car Journey
- On a Train Journey
- On the Motorway
- Sports and Games
- Trees
- Wild Flowers
- Working Vehicles

Tents come in all sorts of shapes and sizes. Some have solid metal poles, others have bendy glassfibre poles. Tent material is usually nylon or cotton and lots of different colours are available.

TUNNEL TENT

Easy to put up with plenty of room for both living and sleeping. Some models have extended porch sections than can be used to store bikes and gear, and do the cooking under cover.

I-SPY points: 10

Date: _____

HOOP TENT

Two or more bendy poles form a long tunnel. These tents give steep walls and good headroom and are light and easy to pack up.

I-SPY points: 10

Date: _____

FRAME TENT

These tents have separate bedrooms, cooking areas, wardrobes and plenty of living and storage space but they are heavy and bulky. Not as popular as they used to be.

I-SPY points: 15

Date: _____

GEODESIC TENT

Mountaineers and explorers use these tents because the four or more interlocking poles give a strong, stable but light tent. This hi-tech model is made from silver fabric to reflect the sun!

I-SPY points: 15

Date: _____

TIPI

The traditional Native American tent is making a bit of a comeback. You can buy your own or rent one for the week at some campsites in Britain.

I-SPY points: 25

Date:

MONGOLIAN YURT

Mongolian nomads sleep in these circular tents all year round – even when it's freezing outside and there is snow on the ground! You can hire these at some campsites and some even have a stove inside!

I-SPY points: 40

Date:

As well as a tent, you need lots of extra bits and pieces to enjoy a camping trip. You'll need somewhere to sit, a stove to cook on, something to keep your food and drink cool and fresh and a nice warm sleeping bag to keep you snug and cosy at night.

CAMPING CHAIRS

Folding chairs come in all sorts of shapes, sizes and colours. Look out for adult chairs and smaller chairs specially designed for children – often in bright colours with cool patterns!

I-SPY points: 10

Date: _____

PICNIC TABLE

Campers often use a combined chair and table kit that folds up nice and small to fit in the car. These are also great for taking on picnics or days out in the country.

I-SPY points: 20

Date: _____

LANTERNS

Once night falls, you'll need something to light up the tent. Most campers have a couple of lanterns that might be powered by batteries, gas or even petrol. Be careful these lanterns can get really hot.

Battery-powered
I-SPY points: 10
Date: _____

Gas/Petrol
I-SPY points: 20
Date: _____

HEAD TORCH

This little device is really useful when you need to keep your hands free. Great for reading.

I-SPY points: 15
Date: _____

7

AIRBED

Sleeping on the ground – even inside a sleeping bag – can be cold and uncomfortable, but if you bring along an inflatable bed, you'll be much happier. It can take a while to pump it up though and remember to check for leaks before you go to bed!

I-SPY points: 10

Date: _____

INFLATABLE SOFA

These inflatable sofas are really comfortable and ideal for use inside or outside the tent. They even have little cut-outs in the arms to keep your cans of drink upright.

I-SPY points: 20

Date: _____

FOOTPUMP

You'll need a pump to blow up those airbeds and sofas. Take it in turns to pump or you'll get really sore legs.

I-SPY points: 15

Date: _____

8

SLEEPING BAG

When it's bed time, after a busy day out in the fresh air, it's great to climb inside a warm and cosy sleeping bag and curl up for the night. The best sleeping bags will even keep you warm in the depths of winter.

I-SPY points: 10

Date:

MALLET

No self-respecting camper would be without one. You really need one to make sure the tent pegs are firmly in the ground.

I-SPY points: 5

Date:

MOSQUITO SQUATTER

Not essential on a camping trip, but a handy way of getting rid of the midges if they start to annoy you!

I-SPY points: 15

Date:

Cooking outdoors is one of the best bits about camping. You always seem be hungrier out in the fresh air and the food always seems to taste better. Most campers cook on a gas stove, but barbecues are also very popular and some campsites even let you cook on a proper campfire. Always take extra care around cookers.

BARBECUE

Barbecues can be either gas or charcoal fired and are great for cooking meat and vegetables in the open air. Some are open while others have lids to keep the heat and smokey flavours in. They do get very hot though, so keep well away when they are lit.

I-SPY points: 10

Date:

CAMPFIRE

Some sites let you make campfires in the evening. Sitting around a glowing campfire toasting bread or marshmallows and telling spooky stories is one of the best parts of camping. Never light fires without permission and always have adults around to help.

I-SPY points: 25

Date:

GAS COOKER

This useful piece of camping kit works just like your stove at home. This one has two burners, so you can heat up some beans and boil the kettle at the same time. Don't meddle with the gas bottle though – it's very dangerous.

I-SPY points: 20

Date: _____

KETTLE

This is an essential bit of kit for making tea for the grown-ups in the morning and a mug of hot cocoa before bed. It's also important to boil your drinking water if you are on an expedition in the wild and getting your water from a stream.

I-SPY points: 10

Date: _____

POTS AND PANS

A barbecue isn't very good for cooking baked beans or stews, so you'll need some pots and pans to pop on the stove to cook these.

I-SPY points: 10

Date: _____

COOLBOX

Milk, butter and meat all need to be kept cool in summer and the best way to keep them fresh is to take a coolbox and keep it cool with plenty of ice or a few freezer blocks.

I-SPY points: 15

Date: _____

FREEZER BLOCKS

Most sites have an ice block exchange system. Take up your defrosted ones and come back with frozen blocks!

I-SPY points: 5

Date: _____

HANGING SHELVES

These shelves are made from light fabric and fold away flat when packed, but provide useful storage space in the camp kitchen.

I-SPY points: 25

Date: _____

There are plenty of things to do inside and outside while on holiday. If it's dry and sunny, a lot of people eat outside. But don't worry if it rains; a cosy caravan lounge is a great place to play board games and read your favourite book.

BICYCLING

Taking a bike is a great way of getting around the campsite and exploring the surrounding countryside. Stay away from main roads though – unless you have an adult with you.

I-SPY points: 10

Date: _____

DINGHY

Taking a rubber dinghy on a camping expedition gives you the chance to explore any lakes or rivers near the campsite – and it will help you stay cool in summer. Always wear a life-jacket.

I-SPY points: 15

Date: _____

FISHING

Lots of campsites are near lakes or rivers and some are almost close enough to let you fish from your tent! Take your fishing rod, just in case...

I-SPY points: 10

Date: _____

BALL GAMES

Football and frisbee are great games for the campsite – this tent even has a special canopy for shooting target practice.

I-SPY points: 10

Date: _____

EAT OUTSIDE

You'll probably see lots of people eating outside if it's sunny. Breakfast outdoors is a great way to start your day – especially with a few rashers of bacon sizzling away on the barbecue. Mmm!

I-SPY points: 20

Date: _____

HIT THE BEACH

If your campsite is near the seaside, you'll be able to spend lots of time on the beach. Some sites are so close to the sea that you can walk straight from your caravan or tent to the beach.

I-SPY points: 20

Date: _____

INDOOR GAMES

When it's wet outside, the best place to be is around the table for a great family board game session. See how many different games you can spot.

I-SPY points: 10

Date: _____

Folding campers are a kind of cross between a caravan and tent. They are packed into their own special trailer, which becomes an integral part of the living area when the tent bit is erected.

CAMP-LET CONCORDE

I-SPY points: 20

Date: _____

CABANON VENUS

I-SPY points: 20

Date: _____

CONWAY CRUSADER

I-SPY points: 20

Date: _____

Caravans come in many shapes and sizes from small two berth to massive twin wheelers. Arrive at the campsite and in minutes you are settled in making a cuppa!

I-SPY points: 10

Date: _____

SPRITE MAJOR 5

Sprite make extremely popular family caravans and you are almost certain to see at least one on most campsites. They are affordable, lightweight and easy to tow with the average family car.

ELDDIS AVANTE

Elddis is another popular make of caravan that you are almost certain to see on British campsites. This is a twin axle 624 with plenty of room for four on board.

I-SPY points: 10

Date: _____

BAILEY PEGASUS

While this Bailey may look like a conventional caravan, the Pegasus actually uses a new high-tech construction system to make it stronger than a conventional caravan.

I-SPY points: 15

Date: _____

ADRIA ADIVA

Adria caravans are made in Slovenia, but are popular with British caravanners. This Adiva has striking tinted windows and if you can sneak a look inside, you'll find a really smart interior.

I-SPY points: 10

Date: _____

ADRIA ACTION

The tiny little Adria Action is one of the coolest caravans on sale in Britain. Its curvy shape and funky lights make it unmistakable, but you will be lucky to see one in Britain as they are quite rare.

I-SPY points: 50

Date: _____

T@B XL

The T@b is known as a Teardrop caravan because of its distinctive shape. They are very aerodynamic and easy to tow, but there isn't a huge amount of living space inside and they are very rare in the UK.

I-SPY points: 50

Date: _____

Modern caravans are warm, comfortable and quite luxurious with many of the appliances and gadgets you would expect to find at home. Inside, you'll find bedrooms, kitchens and bathrooms – they're just a lot smaller than those back at home.

LOUNGE

Most caravans have a lounge area that turns into a bedroom at night. You simply pull out some wooden slats between the settees, rearrange the cushions and you have a big, comfy bed.

I-SPY points: 10

Date:

FIXED BED

More and more caravans now include a fixed bed. It takes a lot of space, but there's usually room to store things underneath and you get a really good night's sleep.

I-SPY points: 20

Date:

MICROWAVE

Lots of caravans have microwaves fitted into their kitchens nowadays. They're ideal for cooking tea when it's raining and too wet for a barbecue outside.

I-SPY points: 20

Date:

BUNK BEDS

Lots of caravans have bunk beds specially designed for children to sleep in. These bunks are quite comfy and often have their own lights and can be curtained off – great for playing on your games console or reading without being disturbed!

I-SPY points: 15, 50 points if you spy triple bunk beds

Date:

FRIDGE

All but the smallest caravans have their own fridges, which are powered by mains electricity, a big battery or gas. They keep food and drink cool and fresh, but they don't usually have as much room as your fridge at home.

I-SPY points: 10

Date:

SHOWER

Many caravans have hot and cold running water, so if you've had a hard day exploring, you can enjoy a nice warm shower in your own caravan – just don't forget to close the cubicle, or you'll get water everywhere!

I-SPY points: 15

Date: _____

FLAT SCREEN TELEVISION

Flat screen televisions are ideal for caravans and they are becoming more and more common. Some even have built-in DVD players, so you can watch movies, too.

I-SPY points: 15
With DVD player: 25

Date: _____

There are some items you simply shouldn't leave home without and there are others that, although not essential, will make any camping trip that little bit more comfortable.

WINDBREAK

A good windbreak is like adding an extra room to your tent and makes sitting outside much more comfortable – especially in the evenings, great at the beach too!

I-SPY points: 10

Date: _____

SOLAR LIGHTS

These lights re-charge themselves during the day and are particularly handy for stopping people tripping over your guyropes in the dark!

I-SPY points: 10

Date: _____

SOLAR SHOWER

Fill this black bag with water and leave it out in the sun and within an hour or so, the water inside will be warm enough to shower with.

I-SPY points: 25

Date: _____

As well as a caravan, there are lots of other things you might need to go caravanning. See how many of these caravan accessories you can spot round and about the campsite.

GAS BOTTLES

Caravans need gas for heating, cooking and in some cases, to power the fridge. The bottles are usually stored in a special locker at the front of the caravan behind the towing hitch.

Calor Gas Bottle
I-SPY points: 10
Date: _____

BP Gas Light
I-SPY points: 20
Date: _____

AWNING

Awnings give caravanners a lot of extra space for living or storage. They might be a full awning, which runs almost the entire length of the caravan, or a porch awning, which just surrounds the door.

I-SPY points: 15
Date: _____

ELECTRIC HOOK-UP

The vast majority of sites now provide electric hook-up (EHU) points for caravans and tents. These provide mains electricity to power everything from the toaster to the telly. Some EHU points have meters to measure the amount of electricity used.

I-SPY points: 10

Date: _____

I-SPY points: 15
Double points for spotting a Winterhoff hitch.

Date: _____

HITCH AND STABILISER

All caravans need a hitch to hook on to the car's towbar so they can be towed. Most of the hitches fitted to British caravans are of the red AL-KO variety, but look carefully and you might spot a blue Winterhoff hitch like the one pictured.

Motorhomes are like vans with a caravan on the back and they are becoming more and more popular in the UK. They range in size from tiny little Micro-campers based on compact delivery vans right up to huge luxury versions based on a bus chassis. See how many different sorts you can spot – both on the road and on a campsite.

MICRO CAMPER

These compact little motorhomes are becoming popular with people who are keen on outdoor sports, but want something a little bit more luxurious than a tent.

The roof lifts up to create extra headroom and there's a sink, gas hob and sometimes even a toilet on board.

I-SPY points: 25

Date: _____

CAMPER VAN

Campers are great for days out, weekends away and even short holidays in the summer. Life is a bit cramped on board, but they have beds, a small kitchen and sometimes even a toilet on board. Look out for classic Volkswagen campers with funky paintwork to get double points.

I-SPY points: 15

Date: _____

25

VAN CONVERSION

This kind of motorhome uses a delivery van like a Ford Transit or Fiat Ducato and converts it for living in. Modern construction techniques are making them more and more luxurious, with a kitchen, toilet, beds and a compact bathroom all crammed inside.

I-SPY points: 20

Date:

I-SPY points: 25

Date:

COACHBUILT MOTORHOME

Coachbuilt motorhomes use a van chassis and fix a separate habitation compartment onto it. It's a bit like taking the wheels off a touring caravan and sticking it onto the back of a delivery van. They generally have more space than campers or van conversions and can be up to 8 metres long with some having a twin axles at the rear.

A-CLASS MOTORHOME

A-class motorhomes are based on a van chassis, but the whole vehicle is coachbuilt, so it doesn't look anything like the vehicle upon which it is based. A-classes are usually quite luxurious inside and many have a big double bed that drops down from the roof of the cab. Like coach built motorhomes, extra-long A-class may have a twin rear axle.

LUXURY LINERS

The biggest and most expensive motorhomes are often called 'Liners'. These luxurious vehicles have all the appliances and gadgets you'll ever need, but they can cost more than a house!

I-SPY points: 30

Date: _____

I-SPY points: 50

Date: _____

I-SPY points: 25

Date: _____

POP TO THE SHOPS

You'll often see motorhomes parked in supermarket car parks while the owners stock up on groceries.

I-SPY points: 25

Date: _____

LOOK IN THE GARAGE

Just like saloon cars have boots, some motorhomes have garages/storage. Some are even big enough to store a scooter, which you can then use to get around on holiday instead of having to drive the motorhome everywhere.

DRIVE-AWAY AWNING

Special motorhome awnings are becoming popular accessories because they extend the amount of living and storage space but can be left on the campsite while your motorhome can be driven away.

I-SPY points: 30

Date: _____

Some people take their caravans and motorhomes across the English Channel and on to the continent. Look out some of these whilst you are travelling to help pass the journey.

BAILEY

ELDDIS

SWIFT

ON THE ROAD

See how many different types of caravan you can spot on the roads and keep a tally of the total numbers of each different make. If you can count more than 25 of any one make, award yourself double points.

I-SPY points:

Bailey 20

Elddis 20

Swift 20

Adria 25

Date: _____

ADRIA

WAITING FOR THE FERRY

If you're waiting to drive onto the ferry, all the caravans will usually park up in the same queue.

Count how many lanes are full of caravans.

I-SPY points:

1 lane 20 points

2 lanes 30 points

3 lanes or more 50 points

Date: _____

AT THE GARAGE

Look out for caravans and motorhomes at filling stations. Caravans need a lot of room to manoeuvre, so most caravanners try to fill up before they hitch up the caravan. Motorhome drivers need to check their vehicle will fit underneath the forecourt canopy.

I-SPY points: 15

Date: _____

CAR WITH BIKES

I-SPY points: 10

Date: _____

CAR WITH BOAT

I-SPY points: 10
Double points for a boat
on a trailer.

Date: _____

CAR WITH ROOFBOX

I-SPY points: 10

Date: _____

Britain has thousands of campsites and there are thousands more on the continent, where camping is even more popular than it is in the UK. Campsites can be little more than a field with a tap in the corner or a fantastic holiday complex with heated swimming pools, cafes, restaurants and bars. Which type will you stay on?

CHECKING IN

When they reach the campsite, caravanners must park their units at the gate and check in at reception before being taken to their pitch. At busy times, you might see lots of caravans waiting to get onto their pitches.

I-SPY points: 15

Date: _____

UNLOADING THE CAR

Once you've arrived at the campsite, there's usually a lot of unloading to be done – especially if you are staying in a tent. A roofbox provides extra space for carrying all those important extras.

I-SPY points: 15

Date: _____

COWS

There are over two million cows in the UK! The most common breed is the black and white Holstein. Jersey cows are sandy in colour and produce extra creamy milk.

I-SPY points: 10

Date: _____

TRACTOR

As farms have got larger so have the tractors needed to work the land. The cab in some is so high up that the driver has to climb up a ladder to get in!

I-SPY points: 10

Date: _____

SHEEP

Sheep are bred for their wool and their meat. Some breeds are very hardy creatures and can survive the harsh winter conditions on mountain and moors.

I-SPY points: 10

Date: _____

DAIRY PARLOUR

This is the name for a set of high-tech machinery that collects the milk from the cows with minimum input from the farmer.

I-SPY points: 20

Date: _____

TITHE BARN

These barns are beautifully constructed and many of them are hundreds of years old. Tithe means 'a tenth' and farmers would have given a proportion of the harvest as payment to the landowner.

I-SPY points: 15

Date: _____

PIGGERY

These strange looking structures are home to the pigs and their piglets. It may be smelly but they are kept dry, are well fed and provided with ample fresh water.

I-SPY points: 10

Date: _____

SILAGE

Silage is grass that has been chopped and fermented to preserve its goodness. It is fed to cattle kept in barns during the cold winter months. You are most likely to see it in the fields wrapped in black plastic.

I-SPY points: 10

Date: _____

WHEAT FIELD WITH POPPIES

As more farms revert to organic farming and stop using herbicides, wheat fields with poppies may once again become a common sight.

I-SPY points: 15

Date: _____

DRY-STONE WALLING

This is the very skillful practice of stacking stones together without the use of mortar. They are very effective and often last for centuries.

I-SPY points: 5

Date: _____

GAME COVER STRIPS

A special mix of seed bearing and dense foliage plants are sown together in strips and are used by game birds for shelter and food during the autumn and winter.

I-SPY points: 20

Date: _____

OILSEED RAPE

It is impossible to miss these colourful fields of bright yellow flowers during early summer.

I-SPY points: 10

Date: _____

CROP BEING SPRAYED

Farmers fight an on-going battle to produce our food in a cost effective manner and most spray crops with chemicals designed to to protect the crop from pests.

I-SPY points: 10

Date: _____

WASHING UP

Modern caravans are fitted with modern appliances, but few have a dishwasher, so someone has to do the dishes the traditional way.

I-SPY points: 10

Date: _____

EMPTYING THE TOILET CASSETTE

Caravans and motorhomes have a special removable tank that can store up to 18 litres of waste but it needs emptying regularly at a special disposal point.

I-SPY points: 15

Date: _____

FILLING THE WATER TANK

Most motorhomes and some caravans have their own water tanks – usually hidden away under one of the seats. These save a lot of trips to the tap to get water, but they still need filling up regularly.

I-SPY points: 15

Date: _____

RIVER FISHING

We have been catching fish from rivers for thousands of years. Once fishing would have been simply to provide food but most anglers now fish for pleasure and some solitude in a beautiful place. Some even fish through the night.

I-SPY points: 15

Date: _____

RIVER EQUIPMENT

A long rod of about three metres will do a good job of keeping the float well away from the bank side bushes and closer to the fish in the middle of the river.

I-SPY points: 15

Date: _____

I-SPY points: 10

Date: _____

TRAWLER AT SEA

Working boats can look a bit scruffy and that's because they are at the mercy of salt water every day. At the end of the season they will be checked and painted ready for the next year.

LOBSTER & CRAB POTS

Modern lobster and crab fishermen tend to use steel and nylon pots but some still use pots made of willow which they make during the winter.

I-SPY points: 20

Date: _____

BEACHCASTING

This is a method of fishing that uses heavy weights, strong line and a strong but flexible rod to cast bait from the beach into the sea. The best casters can cast over 250 metres.

I-SPY points: 10

Date: _____

MACKEREL FISHING

If you cast your feathers out towards where the birds are feeding you will probably encounter a school of mackerel.

I-SPY points: 15

Date: _____

CHARTER BOAT

Should you fail to catch fish from the beach then join a charter and let an experienced skipper take you to a likely spot, maybe over an old wreck.

I-SPY points: 20

Date: _____

COMMERCIAL FISH DOCK

This is where the trawlers and fishermen land their catch to be sold, fresh from the sea.

I-SPY points: 15

Date: _____

TROUT

The brown trout is our native species and the rainbow is an import. You are likely to encounter both in our rivers and lakes.

I-SPY points: 20

Date: _____

CASTING WITH A FLY ROD

Much has been written in an effort to teach the art of casting. The best way to learn is to be shown by an expert and of course, practise makes perfect!

I-SPY points: 20

Date: _____

DRY FLY

There are thousands of different patterns of flies that imitate just about anything that's eaten by trout, salmon and even some sea fish. The flies are made of dyed feathers and silk thread tied around a hook.

I-SPY points: 20

Date: _____

MIRROR CARP

These carp used to be bred in abbey ponds to be eaten on a Friday. Today, fishing for carp has become a multi-million pound industry and people of all ages participate.

I-SPY points: 25

Date: _____

BIVVY & ROD POD

Anglers spend hours trying to land a catch and camp out on the banks of a river or lake in this special kind of tent. They fish with several rods at a time, supported on stands called pods.

I-SPY points: 10

Date: _____

BAIT

Almost anything can be used to catch fish. The only limit is your imagination. The most common baits are bread, worms, maggots, flavoured paste and even tinned luncheon meat!

I-SPY points: 10

Date: _____

Each summer, hundreds of weekend festivals, fayres and shows take place across the UK with thousands of people stopping overnight on huge temporary campsites. Camping at one of these events means you get more time to enjoy the show and meet lots of people with similar interests.

I-SPY points: 25

Date: _____

TENT AND CASTLE

The Gamefair takes place every year at one of England's big stately homes. It's one of the biggest events of the summer with more than 3,000 tents, caravans and motorhomes camping there every year.

Write down the name of the stately home you spot here:

....

COUNTRY FAYRE

Country fayres and county shows have loads of things happening throughout the weekend. You might see heavy horses, falconry displays, terrier racing and fishing demonstrations.

I-SPY points:
Heavy horses 10
Terrier racing 15
Falconry 20
Fishing 25

Date: _____

43

MUSIC FESTIVALS

Music festivals range from huge gatherings like Glastonbury, where famous bands perform live on stage to much smaller events designed to appeal to families, with craft workshops, storytelling and theatre.

Write down who you saw here:............................

I-SPY points:

Craft workshop 10

Storytelling 15

Theatre 20

Famous band 30

Date:_____

44

AGRICULTURAL SHOW

Also called County Shows, they are typified by displays of massive machinery from all the major manufacturers. Also, marquees full of blow-dried and brushed animals all looking their best with their owners hoping for a rosette from the judge.

I-SPY points: 15

Date: _____

PILOT GIG RACING

These sleek boats have been used to rescue stricken crews from sinking vessels but now they are used for pleasure. Regattas are held along many beaches and harbours during the summer season.

I-SPY points: 15

Date: _____

JOGGER

Jogging is just one way of keeping yourself fit. Take advantage of the countryside and jog on holiday along new routes.

I-SPY points: 15

Date: _____

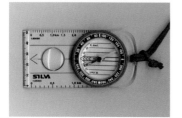

WALKERS COMPASS

If you follow a designated footpath, you may want to use a detailed map and a walkers compass to make sure you go the right way.

I-SPY points: 20

Date: _____

FOOTPATH SIGN

Our nation is criss-crossed by a multitude of footpaths which are open with free rights of way. They are denoted by signs like this one.

I-SPY points: 10

Date: _____

FLASK

The insulation surrounding a flask keeps the contents either hot or cold. Great for hot soup on a cold day!

I-SPY points: 10

Date: _____

STILE

A simple but clever design built in a wall or hedge that allows the easy passage of walkers but not the livestock.

I-SPY points: 10

Date: _____

CYCLE

Cycling is a great way to travel and many people take their bikes with them camping. They offer a great way to see the countryside.

I-SPY points: 10

Date: _____

SADDLE AND TACK

A vital part of owning a pony or horse is looking after the equipment known collectively as tack. The leather needs to be cleaned, nourished and softened with a material called saddle soap which is a mixture of soap oils and beeswax.

I-SPY points: 15

Date: _____

SHIRE HORSES

You are most likely to see a shire horse at a county show where they will be at their best and on display to the public. In some small towns the local brewery may still use them to deliver beer.

I-SPY points: 20

Date: _____

PONY AND TRAP

Once a popular mode of transport, a pony and trap is now rarely seen except at rural shows.

I-SPY points: 15

Date: _____

PONY TREKKING

Some rural areas offer group excursions on horseback. It's a quiet and comfortable way of seeing the countryside from a different perspective.

I-SPY points: 15

Date:

PONY CLUB EVENT

The Pony Club was formed in 1929 and has over 100,000 members. You are most likely to see the members in action as they demonstrate their skills at a local show or Gymkhana.

I-SPY points: 20

Date:

DONKEY RIDES

No summer holiday would be complete without a donkey ride on the beach.

I-SPY points: 10

Date:

Campsites can be big places, with hundreds of pitches for tents, caravans and motorhomes plus chalets and holiday homes, so it's important to know how to find your way around.

I-SPY points: 10

Date: _____

RECEPTION

Most sites have a reception building somewhere near the main entrance. This is where to go if you need to find out where everything is. The helpful people at the reception desk will answer any questions you have.

TOILET BLOCK

All but the smallest sites will have a toilet block where you'll find separate toilets and showers. More and more sites are installing solar panels to heat the water in their shower blocks.

I-SPY points: 10

Date: _____

SWIMMING POOL

Swimming pools are very common on continental sites, where they are usually open air. Larger UK sites are starting to install swimming pools, but they are often indoors, so you can still use them when it rains.

I-SPY points: 20

Date: _____

BESIDE THE SEASIDE

If you're really lucky, you could stay on a site right next to the sea like this Caravan Club site in Scotland.

I-SPY points: 10

Date: _____

CLUB SITES

Some of the best sites in Britain belong to the Caravan Club and the Camping and Caravanning Club. They are well run with good facilities and usually plenty of room to play and explore.

I-SPY points: 25

Date: _____

HOLIDAY COMPLEX

These big complexes are great for families, because there's always something going on whatever the weather and most of them have heated indoor pools.

I-SPY points: 20

Date: _____

BEACH TENT

These handy little pop-up tents can be erected in seconds by just one person. They provide a sand free place for the sandwiches and shelter to keep the drinks cool too. They can even be used to change in.

I-SPY points: 5

Date: _____

WALKING ON THE PIER

The first piers were built In England in 1813 and people have been enjoying them ever since. Today a pier may contain food stalls, gaming arcades or a theatre.

I-SPY points: 10

Date: _____

SLOT MACHINE ARCADE

No seaside would be complete without an amusement arcade. Slot machines are great fun but be careful how much money you spend!

I-SPY points: 5

Date: _____

BEACHCOMBING

Shells of all sizes and colours can be found on the beach. Bonus points for each type found. In this picture a metal detector is being used to find more valuable items.

I-SPY points: 5

Date: _____

ROCKPOOLING

Rockpool water is generally crystal clear and if you are patient little fish, crabs and shrimps will come out of hiding.

I-SPY points: 10

Date: _____

FISH AND CHIPS

Nothing tastes quite as nice as eating fish and chips while dangling your legs over the harbour wall! It's Britain's favourite seaside meal.

I-SPY points: 5

Date:

SANDCASTLES

Everyone loves a sandcastle. Adults change back to being kids again! Who cares if your clothes get a little damp and a bit sandy, it can always be shaken out later.

I-SPY points: 5

Date:

SURFING/ BODYBOARDING

Many beaches are well known for their surf waves. A wetsuit means that you can surf or board most times of the year.

I-SPY points: 10

Date:

SAND ART

If you see a sand artist on the beach, stop and watch for a while. You may learn some new techniques that you can use to create your own masterpiece later in the day.

I-SPY points: 20

Date: _____

FOSSILS

Our coastline is constantly changing as the tides come and go. With a little patience and a sharp pair of eyes you will be amazed what you can discover if you are on the right beach.

I-SPY points: 25

Date: _____

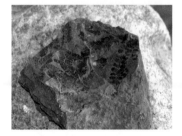

FLYING A KITE

They don't take up much space in the tent or caravan and even a basic kite can be made to dance across the sky. With a little practise the more specialised ones can do amazing stunts.

I-SPY points: 10

Date: _____

BEECH AND BEECHMAST

Beech trees have traditionally been used to make furniture, the off cuts makes excellent firewood. Beechmast (nuts) are harvested by many wild creatures including squirrels, wild boar and deer and a number of different birds.

I-SPY points: 10

Date: _____

YEW AND YEW SEED CAP

The yew is a member of the conifer family. It is slow growing and can live for thousands of years. Seed is stored inside a red berry and sought out by members of the thrush family. Parts of the tree are used to make a medicine to fight cancer.

I-SPY points: 10

Date: _____

HAZEL AND HAZELNUT

A good sign that spring is on the way is when you see catkins on a hazel tree. The ripened hazelnuts are a valuable source of winter food for jays, squirrels and dormice.

I-SPY points: 10

Date: _____

I-SPY points: 10

Date: _____

ENGLISH OAK AND ACORN

The wood from the mighty oak is strong and has been used for centuries in house building, shipbuilding and for making storage barrels. The bark of the oak tree contains tannin which is used in preserving and tanning (dying) leather.

I-SPY points: 10

Date: _____

COMMON ASH AND ASH KEYS

Ash wood can easily be bent when heated with steam and is often used to make handles for tools, sports equipment, furniture and even walking sticks.

HORSE CHESTNUT AND CONKERS

This is probably the tree that boys first learn to recognise. Why? The seeds of the tree are better known as conkers and are great to play with.

I-SPY points: 10

Date: _____

RAGWORT

This plant, which has bright yellow flowers, is a member of the daisy family. The problem is that although it's pretty to look at, it's poisonous and can be fatal, particularly to horses.

I-SPY points: 10

Date:

WOODBINE

This deciduous climber is the wild version of honeysuckle. It produces a heavenly scent mainly at night to attract pollinating insects and produces bright red berries in autumn.

I-SPY points: 10

Date:

CREEPING BUTTERCUP

Beautiful to look at, the buttercup spreads quickly by sending out several runners, each with a baby plant on the end, which send down roots and start the cycle again.

I-SPY points: 10

Date: _____

OX-EYE DAISY

A common and pretty member of the daisy family that will grow almost anywhere and often forms large clumps at the side of the road.

I-SPY points: 5

Date: _____

DOG ROSE

The dog rose has pale pink flowers in summer and in autumn produces bright red hips which contain highly beneficial levels of vitamin C and can be made into a medicinal syrup.

Can you give another name for this rose?

I-SPY points: 5

Double with answer

Date: _____

WATERFALL

Waterfalls occur when over time, a stream of water flows over hard and onto softer rock. The softer material is eroded by the water as it flows downhill.

Where is the largest waterfall in Great Britain?

MOUNTAIN STREAM

Rain falls on to rocky mountain slopes and naturally runs downhill. It collects numerous tiny trickles along the way and eventually becomes a fast flowing stream and then a river.

I-SPY points: 15
Double with answer

Date: _____

I-SPY points: 10

Date: _____

CIRRUS

These thin wispy clouds are often seen high up and are commonly called mare's tails. They often signal the approach of a change in the weather, often for the worse!

I-SPY points: 5

Date:

CUMULONIMBUS

This is the largest cloud formation of all and it can look as if it has a flat top or anvil shape. They can often result in a thunder storm with lightening.

I-SPY points: 5

Date:

CUMULUS

These white, fluffy clouds are usually a indication of good weather. Glider pilots will watch for them as they mean that hot air is rising in thermals.

I-SPY points: 5

Date:

OAST HOUSE

Originally designed for drying hops, as part of brewing, many of these fine buildings are now converted into houses.

I-SPY points: 15

Date: _____

IRRIGATION SPRAY

Crops are sprayed with water to help with their growth, especially in the hot summer months.

I-SPY points: 15

Date: _____

MILLSTONE

These very heaving grinding wheels were once used to grind wheat and other grains.

I-SPY points: 15

Date: _____